Cora's Slate
A Day at Walnut Run School

Story and Photographs by Lynette Leaman Brenneman

Cooper Printing
Lancaster, PA

for my mother

Photo credit: Ethel Landis

My mother attended Refton School, a one-room schoolhouse two
miles southwest of Walnut Run School. She is seen here on her
first day of school in 1955 with Refton School in the background.

Brenneman, Lynette. Cora's Slate: A Day at Walnut Run School / Lynette Brenneman.
Summary: Cora, a student at Walnut Run School, loves her studies and wants to please
her teacher, Miss Edwards. Her mission is disrupted when her slate mysteriously
disappears. This heartwarming story wrestles with a decision Cora must make.

1. Walnut Run School (Lancaster County, Pa.)—Fiction. 2. Children—Pennsylvania—
Lancaster County—Fiction. 3. Rural life—Pennsylvania—Lancaster County—Fiction.
4. Pennsylvania—History—Fiction. 5. Schools, Country—United States—Lancaster
County—History 6. Educational change—United States—History—Juvenile literature.

Printed in the United States of America.
ISBN: 978-0-9859737-2-8

"Good morning, Cora," whispers Landis, my little brother, as he places Fluffy gently on the bed. Every morning, Landis gets up early and tiptoes into our room. Today I awaken first. My sisters, Minnie and Zettie, soon hear Landis and greet Fluffy too.

After breakfast, I visit our cat Tiger and then feed the chickens. My two favorite hens enjoy corn as a special treat.

It is time to leave for school. Landis is sad because we will be gone all day. We assure him we will return before supper, but this fails to cheer him. In hopes of making him happy, I ask if he would like to hear my secret.

I show Landis my pennies and tell him I plan to use them to buy a scholar's companion after school today. That brings a smile to his face. Some of the older girls store their pens and slate pencils in scholar's companions, and Landis knows I have been wishing for one since last term.

We bid
good day
to the
cows but
do not
dawdle
because
we want
to arrive
at school
on time.

As I approach the schoolyard, Marian and Ada run to me with a piece of string, begging me to teach them cat's cradle.

Ring! Miss Edwards sounds the bell at eight o'clock sharp, and we quickly line up to enter the school in an orderly fashion.

I place my
lunch pail
and hat in
the cloak
room and
greet my
good friend
Isabelle.

While Daniel shovels coal into the stove to take the chill out of the air, I notice Nancy showing Anne her new scholar's companion. I touch the coin purse in my pocket and look forward to buying my own scholar's companion later today.

Miss Edwards greets us. We reply in unison, "Good morning, Miss Edwards." She calls roll and asks Frank where his older brothers are. He replies that they were kept home to help with shearing sheep today.

Miss Edwards reads aloud from the Bible. We extend our right hands toward the flag as we recite the Pledge of Allegiance. Then we say the Lord's Prayer together. Next Miss Edwards calls my class to assemble on the recitation bench for our reading lesson.

The Lord's Prayer

Our Father which art in heaven,
Hallowed be thy name.

Thy kingdom come,

Thy will be done in earth
as it is in heaven.

Give us this day our daily bread.

And forgive us our debts,
as we forgive our debtors.

And lead us not into temptation,
but deliver us from evil:

For thine is the kingdom, and the
power, and the glory for ever.

Amen.

- Matthew 6:9b-13 (KJV)

We sing while Miss Edwards
accompanies us on the piano.
My favorite song is "My
Country 'tis of Thee."

My Country 'tis of Thee

My country 'tis of thee

Sweet land of liberty

Of thee I sing

Land where my fathers died

Land of the pilgrim's pride

From ev'ry mountainside

Let freedom ring

- Samuel Francis Smith

After we finish singing, I search my desk for my slate. It is missing!

I tell Miss Edwards about my lost slate, and she grants me permission to share with Minnie.

Copying problems from the board, we diligently figure arithmetic on slates while Miss Edwards checks our work. I prefer written computation, but Minnie excels at mental arithmetic. Miss Edwards drills us with mental arithmetic questions between classes, and Minnie is usually quick to answer first.

Miss Edwards is the nicest teacher we have ever had, and I do not want to disappoint her. Has my missing slate displeased her?

I am thankful to share Minnie's slate, but as I work, I wonder where my slate might be. Could someone have taken it?

Mulberry Bush

*Here we go 'round
the mulberry bush,
the mulberry bush,
the mulberry bush.
Here we go 'round
the mulberry bush
on a cold and frosty morning.*

- Folk Song

At recess, the boys use the outhouse roof to play cully over. Sometimes they try to catch fish with their bare hands in the run beside the school. The younger girls sing "Mulberry Bush." I like to jump rope. The older girls do not play at all. They just stand around and chat. I have no idea how they always have so much to discuss.

After recess, I help Benjamin with arithmetic.

Caroline listens to me read while Miss Edwards teaches other grades. I enjoy reading to Caroline. I think she is sophisticated. Caroline was the first girl at school to own a scholar's companion.

Geography is my favorite subject because I wish I could travel to the faraway places we learn about. We are studying the countries in Europe.

We eat lunch during our intermission. Some students walk home for lunch. My sisters and I carry our lunch to school in pails and eat on the front steps with friends. Today we share our apple turnovers with the other girls. I tell Abigail about the pennies I have saved to buy a scholar's companion. She is excited to see it.

Carrie, Mary, Elsie, and I play jacks after
lunch. I ask the girls about my slate, but they
tell me they do not know what happened to it.

After lunch, I need to copy a sentence on each of the 18 lines in my penmanship book. I do not enjoy writing, and I worry I will blot the ink.

Miss Edwards asks Zettie and Nancy to do recitations for the class. Zettie delivers the poem "My Shadow," by Robert Louis Stevenson, and Nancy recites Psalm 100. I hope Miss Edwards chooses me next time. I recently learned "The Sparrow's Nest," by Mary Botham Howitt.

Psalm 100

Make a joyful noise unto the Lord, all ye lands.
Serve the Lord with gladness:
come before his presence with singing.
Know ye that the Lord he is God:
it is he that hath made us, and not we ourselves;
we are his people, the sheep of his pasture.
Enter into his gates with thanksgiving,
and into his courts with praise:
be thankful unto him, and bless his name.
For the Lord is good; his mercy is everlasting;
and his truth endureth to all generations.

(KJV)

While I am at the water bucket getting a drink, Seth informs me he spied George using my slate. I nearly spill what is left of my water. So that is what happened to my slate! Seth says he will report what he saw to Miss Edwards.

Miss Edwards calls George to the front of the room. I cannot hear what she says to him, but she looks upset.

After Miss Edwards talks to George, he reluctantly returns my slate. I feel sorry for him when I remember he lost his slate. I know George's family does not have enough money to purchase a new one.

At the end of the day, we compete in a spelling bee. Miss Edwards asks me to spell the word *companion*. I spell it correctly, and it makes me think about the scholar's companion I will soon own.

As we leave school, I notice George stays behind to sweep the floor.

My sisters and I walk to the store in Refton. Madam Emma Rose, the storekeeper, shows me a beautiful scholar's companion. It is exactly what I have been wanting! As I touch the shiny wood, I think of George and his lost slate. I remember the sad look in his eyes as he returned my slate to me.

Then I notice a smaller scholar's companion. It is a simple turned-wood case. If I buy this instead of the beautiful wooden one, would I also be able to purchase a slate for George?

Madam Rose counts my pennies. Yes! I have enough money. I decide to purchase the turned-wood case and a slate for George.

I think about the decision I have made while showing my purchases to my sisters. Minnie reminds me that George had to stay after school to sweep, so we hurry to meet him as he walks home.

George's face beams when I hand him the slate. I realize it is truly more blessed to give than to receive.

My sisters and I review our day as we stroll home. Landis jumps up and down as soon as he sees us and begs to see my scholar's companion. I can tell he is disappointed that I bought only a small turned-wood case, but I am deeply satisfied. My decision to buy the slate for George made us both happy.

Minnie, Zettie, and I say our prayers before bed.
I thank God for helping me to make my decision.
I am grateful for my family,
my wonderful teacher, and
Walnut Run School.

Ashlyn portrays her great-great-grandmother, Cora Groff Herr, who attended Walnut Run School. Ashlyn plays the saxophone. She also enjoys board games such as checkers and chess. She likes to swim and sew, and she sewed the nightgown she wears in this book. Ashlyn liked playing with her friends during the photo shoot.

Edith portrays Cora's sister Minnie. She plays violin. Edith enjoys grooming and riding her horse. She liked seeing what a school day might have looked like for her great-great-grandmother, Minnie Rohrer Witmer, who attended Walnut Run School. Edith enjoyed using the slate and slate pencil.

Sarah (Ashlyn's real-life sister) portrays Cora's sister, Luzetta (Zettie). Sarah's great-great-grandmother, Cora Groff Herr, attended Walnut Run. Sarah enjoys playing piano, doing art projects, and playing hopscotch. She sewed the dress and nightgown she wears in this book. She enjoyed playing with her friends at the schoolhouse.

Ezra portrays Cora's little brother, Landis. Ezra likes to swim, help his mommy make cookies and crepes, play games with his daddy, and play outside.

Annika likes to color, play games, read, swim, and play with her cat, Tybalt. Annika delighted in watching the cows run in the field across from the schoolhouse.

Benjamin enjoys arts and crafts, hunting for treasures, spending time in nature, and learning about animals. He liked experiencing an old schoolhouse.

Caroline plays piano. She can be found playing kickball, riding her bicycle, and sewing. Caroline liked her costume and the schoolhouse.

Maria portrays her great-grandmother, Mary Rohrer Burkhart, who attended Walnut Run. Maria spends time reading and exploring nature. She likes animals, bugs, drawing, coloring, and working on the farm. She enjoyed writing on a slate and eating her old-fashioned school lunch, especially the apple turnover.

Jesse portrays his great-grandfather, E. Frank Deiter, who attended Walnut Run School. Jesse is a bookworm and piano player. Playing cully over during the photo session was a highlight.

Davison plays soccer, trumpet, and violin. His favorite subjects are math and history. Learning about how the students dressed and lived fascinated him. He enjoyed playing cully over at recess.

Misty's great-grandmother, Nancy Witmer Frey, attended Walnut Run. Misty plays the bells and soccer and likes being outside and romping with her dog. The old school books piqued Misty's interest. She also enjoyed eating an apple turnover at lunchtime.

Seth's great-grandfather, E. Frank Deiter, attended Walnut Run School. Seth can often be found taking apart engines, riding bike, or playing piano. Cully over was a highlight of the photo shoot.

Isabelle enjoys drawing, crafts, dressing up, and playing make believe. She also plays the piano. Isabelle liked saying the pledge during the book photography.

Magdalena plays soccer and enjoys reading, riding her bike, and carrying her pet chicken. The design of Magdalena's costume was based on the school photo of her great-great-grandmother, Ada Kreider Gochnauer. She enjoyed playing at the creek near the schoolhouse.

Selah likes to color, draw, paint, and swim. Selah enjoyed catching grasshoppers and throwing rocks into the creek at Walnut Run during breaks between photos.

Abigail enjoys playing soccer and reading. She likes animals and hopes for a pet rabbit someday. Abigail liked spending time with her friends at the schoolhouse.

Anne enjoys raising sheep to show at the fair. She plays softball and piano, likes to draw, enjoys science, and wants to be a nurse when she grows up. Anne liked the costumes and making new friends at the schoolhouse.

Jenna portrays her great-grandmother, Nancy Witmer Frey, who attended Walnut Run School. Jenna plays baritone horn, volleyball, and soccer. She enjoys arts and crafts and loves to play with her dog, Bella. The old school supplies were fascinating to her.

Colson plays soccer, basketball, baritone horn, and bass guitar. Colson enjoyed making new friends and playing games with the other boys at recess. A highlight for him was when Mr. Shurr visited and shared about teaching at Walnut Run School.

Caroline enjoys singing, acting, spending time with friends, and playing soccer. She loved her costume. It was exciting for Caroline to see what life was like long ago, and she enjoyed making new friends.

Carly's great-grandmother, Nancy Witmer Frey, attended Walnut Run School. Carly plays flute, volleyball, and lacrosse. Carly enjoyed seeing the schoolhouse and dressing up.

Elijah plays percussion in the school band and enjoys playing soccer. Spending time with family and friends and being at home are meaningful to him. Elijah enjoyed making friends with the other students and loved eating apple turnovers.

Allen's great-great-grandmother, Minnie Rohrer Witmer, attended Walnut Run. His family saved Minnie's report card, which includes the name of her teacher, Miss Lydia Edwards. He enjoys farming, hunting, fishing, and being outdoors. Allen liked making new friends at the schoolhouse.

Angie portrays Miss Lydia Edwards, who taught Angie's husband's great-grandmother, Minnie Rohrer Witmer, at Walnut Run School. Angie enjoys spending time with her husband and children. Angie delighted in seeing the lovely old schoolhouse come to life. She had never worn a corset before but noted it certainly encouraged good posture.

Walnut Run School is named for the creek that flows beside the school. It was built in Strasburg Township, Lancaster County, Pennsylvania, in 1879. Susan Hendricks Barry taught the final class at Walnut Run School, which closed in 1994.

Sheila portrays Madam Emma Rose, proprietor of the Refton Store. She teaches Spanish and enjoys spending time with family and friends. In her spare time Sheila loves to travel, hike, cook ethnic foods, camp, garden, and read.

Mr. Larry Shurr, who taught at Walnut Run School from 1963 to 1970, visited during the photography session and talked to the students about the school and his experiences there.

Photo credit: Carol Leaman

Photo credit: Carol Landis Leaman

The Refton General Store was operated by George T. and Emma Rose. This photo shows Raymond B. Reinhart, a later owner, in 1963. Store photos were taken at the Country Store at Landis Valley Museum.

Cora's Slate is a fictional story about a real girl. Cora Groff Herr is the author's great-grandmother. She had three siblings, Luzetta (Zettie), Minnie, and Landis. All four Groff children attended Walnut Run School.

Photo courtesy of Carol Leaman

Print Resources:

Apps-Bodilly, S. (2013). *One Room Schools*. Madison, WI: Wisconsin Historical Society Press.

Bail, R. (1999). *One-Room School*. Boston, MA: Houghton Mifflin Company.

Blaisdell, A. F. (1891). *The Child's Book of Health*. New York, NY: Ginn & Company.

Fish, D. W. (1877). *The Complete Arithmetic, Oral and Written*. New York, NY: Ivison, Blakeman, Taylor & Co.

Fletcher, S. W. (1955). *Pennsylvania Agriculture and Country Life: 1840-1940*. Harrisburg, PA: Pennsylvania Historical and Museum Commission.

Grove, M. J. (2000). *Legacy of One-Room Schools*. Morgantown, PA: Masthof Press.

Hartford, E. F. (1977). *The Little White Schoolhouse*. Lexington, KY: University Press of Kentucky.

Herr, D. W. (1994). *A Century of Education: Cross Roads School*. Ephrata, PA: Grace Press.

Israel, F. L. (Ed.) (1968). *1897 Sears, Roebuck Catalogue*. Philadelphia, PA: Chelsea House Publishers.

Kellogg, A. M. (1884). *School Management: A Practical Guide for the Teacher in the School-Room*. New York, NY: E. L. Kellogg & Co.

McGuffey, W. H. (Ed.) (1920). *McGuffey's Eclectic Readers*. New York, NY: H. H. Vail.

Phillips, J. (2002). *School Days Long Ago*. Columbus, OH: McGraw Hill.

Pringle, L. (1998). *One Room School*. Honesdale, PA: Boyds Mills Press.

Rocheleau, P. (2007). *The One-Room Schoolhouse*. New York, NY: Universe Publishing.

Shelley, M. V. (2015). *Lancaster County's One-Room Schools and the History of the Common School Movement*. Lancaster, PA: LancasterHistory.org.

Sloane, E. (1972). *The Little Red Schoolhouse*. Mineola, NY: Dover Publications.

Stein, G. S. (1994). *Country Legacy: Lancaster County One-Room Schools*. Lancaster, PA: Brookshire Printing, Inc.

Swinton, W. (1872). *Word-Book of English Spelling, Oral and Written*. New York, NY: Ivison, Blakeman & Company.

Photo courtesy of Jim Groff

The Groff home was built in 1892 by Cora Groff's parents, Henry and Anna Groff. Cora lived on the farm on Lime Valley Road with her parents and her siblings. Groff home photos were taken on location.

Lynette Brenneman is a native of Lancaster County. For 28 years, she lived two houses away from Oak Grove School, an actively used one-room country schoolhouse that has since been torn down. She holds bachelor's and master's degrees in elementary education and taught third grade for 12 years. She enjoyed teaching her own students at Walnut Run School when she took them there for a day of learning.

Photo credit: Durelle Leaman